Easy to Play Carols

Arranged for Piano by
Alan Ridout

Kevin Mayhew

We hope you enjoy *Easy to Play Carols*.
Further copies are available from your local music shop.

In case of difficulty, please contact the publisher direct:

The Sales Department
KEVIN MAYHEW LTD
Rattlesden
Bury St Edmunds
Suffolk IP30 0SZ

Phone 0449 737978
Fax 0449 737834

Please ask for our complete catalogue of outstanding Instrumental Music.

Front Cover: *Carol Singing* (Anonymous).
Reproduced by kind permission of Fine Art Photographic Library, London.

Cover designed by Juliette Clarke and Graham Johnstone.
Picture Research: Jane Rayson.

First published in Great Britain in 1993 by Kevin Mayhew Ltd.

© Copyright 1993 Kevin Mayhew Ltd.

ISBN 0 86209 457 7

All or part of these pieces have been arranged by Alan Ridout
and are the copyright of Kevin Mayhew Ltd.

Music Editor: Anthea Smith.
Music Setting: Louise Hill.

Printed and bound in Great Britain.

Contents

HARK, THE HERALD ANGELS SING

1. Hark, the herald angels sing glory to the new-born king; peace on earth and mercy mild, God and sinners reconciled: joyful all ye nations rise, join the triumph of the skies, with th'angelic host proclaim Christ is born in Bethlehem. *Refrain* Hark, the herald angels sing glory to the new-born king.

2. Christ, by highest heaven adored,
   Christ, the everlasting Lord;
   late in time behold him come,
   offspring of a virgin's womb!
   Veiled in flesh the Godhead see,
   hail, the incarnate Deity!
   Pleased as man with man to dwell,
   Jesus, our Emmanuel.

3. Hail the heaven-born prince of peace!
   Hail the sun of righteousness!
   Light and life to all he brings,
   risen with healing in his wings;
   mild he lays his glory by,
   born that man no more may die,
   born to raise the sons of earth,
   born to give them second birth.

Text: Charles Wesley (1707 - 1788) and others
Melody: Felix Mendelssohn (1809 - 1847)

SUSSEX CAROL

2. Then why should men on earth be so sad,
   since our redeemer made us glad, (*repeat*)
   when from our sin he set us free,
   all for to gain our liberty?

3. When sin departs before his grace,
   then life and health come in its place; (*repeat*)
   angels and men with joy may sing,
   all for to see the new-born king.

4. All out of darkness we have light,
   which made the angels sing this night: (*repeat*)
   'Glory to God and peace to men,
   now and for evermore. Amen.'

Text and Melody: Traditional English

THE ANGEL GABRIEL

1. The an - gel Ga - bri - el from hea - ven came, his wings as drift - ed snow, his

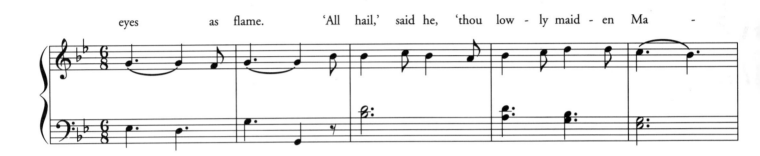

eyes as flame. 'All hail,' said he, 'thou low - ly maid - en Ma -

ry, most high - ly fa - voured la - dy.' Glo - ri - a!

2. 'For known a blessed mother thou shalt be,
   all generations laud and honour thee.
   Thy son shall be Emmanuel, by seers foretold.
   Most highly favoured lady.' Gloria!

3. Then gentle Mary meekly bowed her head,
   'to me be as it pleaseth God,' she said.
   'My soul shall laud and magnify his holy name.'
   Most highly favoured lady. Gloria!

4. Of her, Emmanuel, the Christ, was born
   in Bethlehem, all on a Christmas morn,
   and Christian folk throughout the world will ever say:
   Most highly favoured lady. Gloria!

Text: Sabine Baring-Gould (1834 - 1924)
Melody: Basque Folk Tune

RISE UP, SHEPHERD, AND FOLLOW

2. If you take good heed of the angel's words,
   rise up, shepherd, and follow,
   you'll forget your flocks, you'll forget your herds,
   rise up, shepherd, and follow.

Text and Melody: American Spiritual

ONCE IN ROYAL DAVID'S CITY

2. He came down to earth from heaven
   who is God and Lord of all,
   and his shelter was a stable,
   and his cradle was a stall;
   with the poor and mean and lowly
   lived on earth our Saviour holy.

3. And through all his wondrous childhood
   he would honour and obey,
   love, and watch the lowly maiden
   in whose gentle arms he lay:
   Christian children all must be
   mild, obedient, good as he.

4. For he is our childhood's pattern,
   day by day like us he grew;
   he was little, weak, and helpless,
   tears and smiles like us he knew;
   and he feeleth for our sadness,
   and he shareth in our gladness.

5. And our eyes at last shall see him
   through his own redeeming love;
   for that child so dear and gentle
   is our Lord in heaven above;
   and he leads his children on
   to the place where he is gone.

6. Not in that poor lowly stable,
   with the oxen standing by,
   we shall see him, but in heaven,
   set at God's right hand on high;
   where like stars his children crowned
   all in white shall wait around.

Text: Cecil Frances Alexander (1818 - 1895)
Melody: Henry John Gauntlett (1805 - 1876)

WHAT CHILD IS THIS?

1. What child is this, who, laid to rest, on Ma - ry's lap is sleep - ing? Whom

an - gels greet with an - thems sweet, while shep - herds watch are keep - ing?

This, this is Christ the king, whom shep - herds guard and an - gels sing:

come, greet the in - fant Lord, the babe, the son of Ma - ry!

2. Why lies he in such mean estate,
where ox and ass are feeding?
Good Christians, fear! for sinners here
the silent Word is pleading.
Nails, spear shall pierce him through,
the cross be borne for me, for you:
hail, hail the Word made flesh,
the babe, the son of Mary!

3. So bring him incense, gold and myrrh,
all tongues and peoples own him.
The King of kings salvation brings,
let every heart enthrone him:
raise, raise your song on high,
while Mary sings a lullaby;
joy, joy for Christ is born,
the babe, the son of Mary.

Text: William Chatterton Dix (1837 - 1898)
Melody: Traditional English

O COME, EMMANUEL

2. O come, thou Rod of Jesse, free
   thine own from Satan's tyranny;
   from depths of hell thy people save,
   and give them victory o'er the grave.

3. O come, thou Dayspring, come and cheer
   our spirits by thine advent here;
   disperse the gloomy clouds of night,
   and death's dark shadows put to flight.

4. O come, thou key of David, come
   and open wide our heavenly home;
   make safe the way that leads on high,
   and close the path to misery.

5. O come, O come, thou Lord of Might,
   who to thy tribes on Sinai's height
   in ancient times didst give the law
   in cloud and majesty and awe.

Text: Translated from the Latin by John Mason Neale (1818 - 1866)
Melody: Adapted from a French Missal by Thomas Helmore (1811 - 1890)

I SAW THREE SHIPS

1. I saw three ships come sail - ing in, on Christ - mas Day, on Christ - mas Day. I

saw three ships come sail - ing in, on Christ - mas Day in the morn - ing.

2. And what was in those ships all three?
   On Christmas Day, on Christmas Day.
   And what was in those ships all three?
   On Christmas Day in the morning.

3. Our Saviour Christ and his lady,
   on Christmas Day, on Christmas Day.
   Our Saviour Christ and his lady,
   on Christmas Day in the morning.

4. Pray whither sailed those ships all three?
   On Christmas Day, on Christmas Day.
   Pray whither sailed those ships all three?
   On Christmas Day in the morning.

5. O they sailed into Bethlehem,
   on Christmas Day, on Christmas Day.
   O they sailed into Bethlehem,
   on Christmas Day in the morning.

6. And all the bells on earth shall ring,
   on Christmas Day, on Christmas Day.
   And all the bells on earth shall ring,
   on Christmas Day in the morning.

7. And all the angels in heav'n shall sing,
   on Christmas Day, on Christmas Day.
   And all the angels in heav'n shall sing,
   on Christmas Day in the morning.

8. And all the souls on earth shall sing,
   on Christmas Day, on Christmas Day.
   And all the souls on earth shall sing,
   on Christmas Day in the morning.

9. Then let us all rejoice amain!
   On Christmas Day, on Christmas Day.
   Then let us all rejoice amain!
   On Christmas Day in the morning.

Text and Melody: Traditional English

GOOD KING WENCESLAS

1. Good King Wen - ces - las looked out on the Feast of Ste - phen,

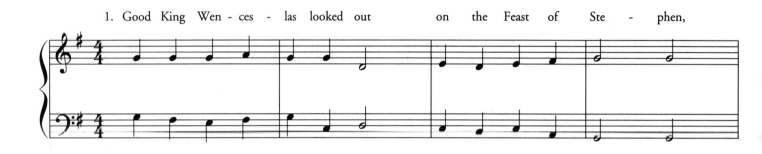

when the snow lay round a - bout, deep, and crisp, and e - ven:

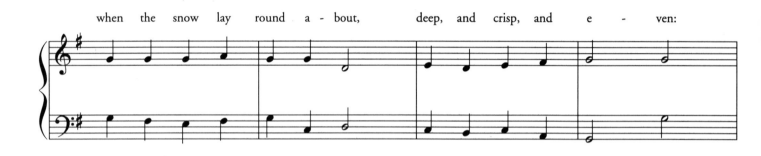

bright - ly shone the moon that night, though the frost was cru - el,

when a poor man came in sight, gath-'ring win - ter fu - el.

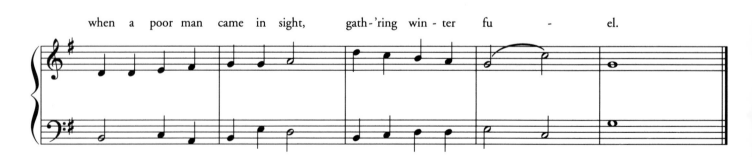

2. 'Hither, page, and stand by me,
   if thou know'st it, telling:
   yonder peasant, who is he,
   where and what his dwelling?'
   'Sire, he lives a good league hence,
   underneath the mountain;
   right against the forest fence
   by Saint Agnes' fountain.'

3. 'Bring me flesh, and bring me wine,
   bring me pine-logs hither:
   thou and I will see him dine
   when we bear them thither.'
   Page and monarch forth they went,
   forth they went together,
   through the rude wind's wild lament
   and the bitter weather.

4. 'Sire, the night is darker now,
   and the wind blows stronger;
   fails my heart, I know not how;
   I can go no longer.'
   'Mark my footsteps, good my page,
   tread thou in them boldly:
   thou shalt find the winter's rage
   freeze thy blood less coldly.'

5. In his master's steps he trod
   where the snow lay dinted;
   heat was in the very sod
   which the saint had printed.
   Therefore, Christians all, be sure,
   wealth or rank possessing,
   ye who now will bless the poor
   shall yourselves find blessing.

Text: From *Piae Cantiones* (1582) translated by John Mason Neale (1818 - 1866)
Melody: Traditional English

CHILD IN THE MANGER

1. Child in the man - ger, in-fant of Ma - ry; out-cast and strang - er, Lord of all; child who in-he - rits all our trans-gres - sions, all our de - me - rits on him fall.

2. Once that most holy child of salvation
   gentle and lowly lived below;
   now as our glorious mighty Redeemer,
   see him victorious o'er each foe.

3. Prophets foretold him, infant of wonder;
   angels behold him on his throne;
   worthy our Saviour of all their praises;
   happy for ever are his own.

Text: Mary Macdonald (1817 - 1890) translated by Lachlan Macbean (1853 - 1931)
Melody: Traditional Gaelic

IT CAME UPON THE MIDNIGHT CLEAR

2. Still through the cloven skies they come,
with peaceful wings unfurled;
and still their heavenly music floats
o'er all the weary world:
above its sad and lowly plains
they bend on hovering wing;
and ever o'er its Babel-sounds
the blessed angels sing.

3. Yet with the woes of sin and strife
the world has suffered long;
beneath the angel-strain have rolled
two thousand years of wrong;
and man, at war with man, hears not
the love-song which they bring:
O hush the noise, ye men of strife,
and hear the angels sing.

4. For lo, the days are hastening on,
by prophet bards foretold,
when, with the ever-circling years,
comes round the age of gold;
when peace shall over all the earth
its ancient splendours fling,
and the whole world give back the song
which now the angels sing.

Text: Edmund Hamilton Sears (1810 - 1876)
Melody: Traditional English adapted Arthur Sullivan (1842 - 1900)

PAST THREE O'CLOCK

Refrain

Past three o' - clock, and a cold, fros - ty morn - ing! Past three o' -

clock! Good mor - row, mas - ters all! 1. Born is a ba - by, gen - tle as

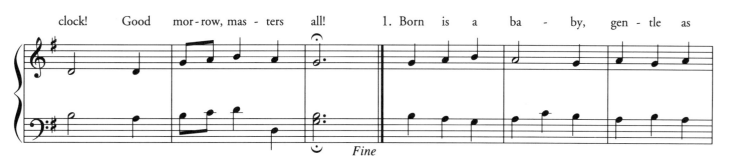

Fine

may be, son of th'e - ter - nal Fa - ther su - per - nal.

D.C. al Fine

2. Seraph choir singeth,
   angel bell ringeth:
   hark how they rhyme it,
   time it, and chime it.

3. Mid earth rejoices
   hearing such voices
   ne'ertofore so well
   carolling 'Nowell!'

4. Light out of starland
   leadeth from far land
   princes, to meet him,
   worship and greet him.

5. Myrrh from full coffer,
   incense they offer:
   nor is the golden
   nugget withholden.

6. Thus they: I pray you,
   up, sirs, nor stay you
   till ye confess him
   likewise, and bless him.

Text: George Ratcliffe Woodward (1848 - 1934)
Melody: Traditional English

A VIRGIN MOST PURE

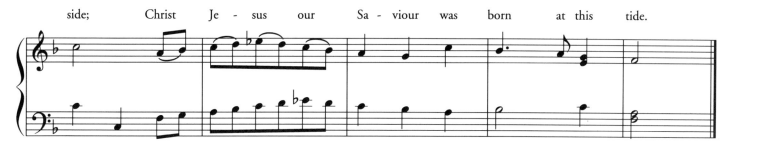

side; Christ Je - sus our Sa - viour was born at this tide.

2. In Bethlehem Jewry a city there was,
   where Joseph and Mary together did pass,
   and there to be taxed with many one mo',
   for Caesar commanded the same should be so.

3. But when they had entered the city so fair,
   a number of people so mighty was there,
   that Joseph and Mary, whose substance was small,
   could find in the inn there no lodging at all.

4. Then they were constrained in a stable to lie,
   where horses and asses they used for to tie;
   their lodgings so simple they took it no scorn,
   but against the next morning our Saviour was born.

5. The King of all kings to this world being brought,
   small store of fine linen to wrap him was sought;
   and when she had swaddled her young son, so sweet,
   within an ox-manger she laid him to sleep.

6. Then God sent an angel from heaven so high
   to certain poor shepherds in fields where they lie,
   and bade them no longer in sorrow to stay,
   because that our Saviour was born on this day.

7. Then presently after the shepherds did spy
   a number of angels that stood in the sky;
   they joyfully talked and sweetly did sing,
   'to God be all glory, our heavenly King.'

Text and Melody: Traditional English

MARY HAD A BABY

1. Ma - ry had a ba - by, yes, Lord, Ma - ry had a ba - by, yes, my Lord,

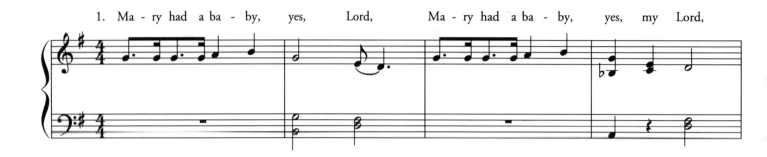

Ma - ry had a ba - by, yes, Lord! The peo - ple keep a - com - ing, but the train has gone!

2. What did she name him, yes, Lord,
what did she name him, yes, my Lord,
what did she name him, yes, Lord?
The people keep a-coming,
but the train has gone!

3. Mary named him Jesus, yes, Lord,
Mary named him Jesus, yes, my Lord,
Mary named him Jesus, yes, Lord!
The people keep a-coming,
but the train has gone!

4. Where was he born, yes, Lord,
where was he born, yes, my Lord,
where was he born, yes, Lord?
The people keep a-coming,
but the train has gone!

5. Born in a stable, yes, Lord,
born in a stable, yes, my Lord,
born in a stable, yes, Lord!
The people keep a-coming,
but the train has gone!

6. Where did she lay him, yes, Lord,
where did she lay him, yes, my Lord,
where did she lay him, yes, Lord?
The people keep a-coming,
but the train has gone!

7. Laid him in a manger, yes, Lord,
laid him in a manger, yes, my Lord,
laid him in a manger, yes, Lord!
The people keep a-coming,
but the train has gone!

Text and Melody: Traditional West Indian

LITTLE JESUS, SWEETLY SLEEP

1. Lit - tle Je - sus, sweet - ly sleep, do not stir, we will lend a coat of fur;

we will rock you, rock you, rock you, we will rock you, rock you, rock you:

see the fur to keep you warm, snug - ly round your ti - ny form.

2. Mary's little baby sleep, sweetly sleep,
sleep in comfort, slumber deep;
we will rock you, rock you, rock you,
we will rock you, rock you, rock you:
we will serve you all we can,
darling, darling little man.

Text: Translated from the Czech by Percy Dearmer (1867 - 1936)
Melody: Traditional Czech

WE THREE KINGS

2. Born a king on Bethlehem's plain,
   gold I bring, to crown him again:
   King for ever, ceasing never,
   over us all to reign.

3. Frankincense to offer have I,
   incense owns a deity nigh:
   prayer and praising, all men raising,
   worship him, God most high!

4. Myrrh is mine; it's bitter perfume
   breathes a life of gathering gloom:
   sorrowing, sighing, bleeding, dying,
   sealed in the stone cold tomb.

5. Glorious now behold him arise,
   King and God and sacrifice!
   Heaven sings: 'Alleluia!'
   'Alleluia!' the earth replies.

Text and Melody: John Henry Hopkins (1820 - 1891)

UNTO US IS BORN A SON

2. Christ, from heav'n descending low,
   comes on earth a stranger:
   ox and ass their owner know,
   becradled in the manger,
   becradled in the manger.

3. This did Herod sore affray,
   and grievously bewilder,
   so he gave the word to slay,
   and slew the little childer,
   and slew the little childer.

4. Of his love and mercy mild
   this the Christmas story,
   and O that Mary's gentle child
   might lead us up to glory!
   might lead us up to glory!

5. 'O' and 'A', and 'A' and 'O'
   cum cantibus in choro;
   let the merry organ go,
   Benedicamus Domino,
   Benedicamus Domino.

Text: Translated from the Latin by George Ratcliffe Woodward (1848 - 1934)
Melody: From *Piae Cantiones* (1582)

THE HOLLY AND THE IVY

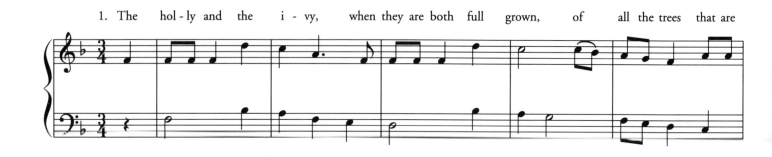

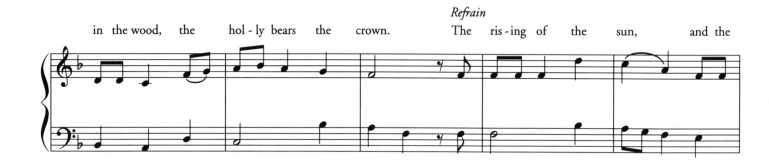

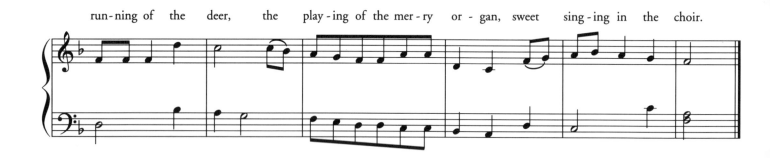

2. The holly bears a blossom
   as white as the lily flower,
   and Mary bore sweet Jesus Christ
   to be our sweet Saviour.

3. The holly bears a berry
   as red as any blood,
   and Mary bore sweet Jesus Christ
   to do poor sinners good.

4. The holly bears a prickle
   as sharp as any thorn,
   and Mary bore sweet Jesus Christ
   on Christmas Day in the morn.

5. The holly bears a bark
   as bitter as any gall,
   and Mary bore sweet Jesus Christ
   for to redeem us all.

Text: Traditional English Carol collected by Cecil Sharp (1859 - 1924)
Melody: Traditional English

IN THE BLEAK MID-WINTER

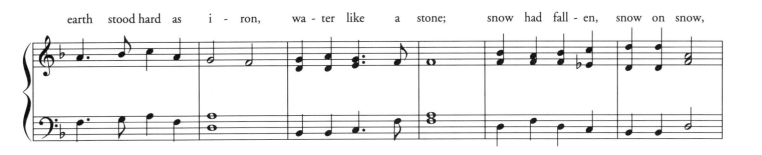

2. Our God, heav'n cannot hold him nor earth sustain;
heav'n and earth shall flee away when he comes to reign:
in the bleak mid-winter a stable place sufficed
the Lord God almighty, Jesus Christ.

3. Enough for him, whom cherubim worship night and day,
a breastful of milk and a manger full of hay;
enough for him, whom angels fall down before,
the ox and ass and camel which adore.

4. Angels and archangels may have gathered there,
Cherubim and Seraphim thronged the air:
but only his mother in her maiden bliss
worshipped the beloved with a kiss.

5. What can I give him, poor as I am?
If I were a shepherd I would bring a lamb;
if I were a wise man I would do my part;
yet what I can I give him, give him my heart.

Text: Christina Rossetti (1830 - 1894)
Melody: Gustav Holst (1874 - 1934)

I WONDER AS I WANDER

1. I won-der as I wan-der, out un-der the sky, how Je-sus the Sa-viour did come for to die for

poor ord'n-'ry peo-ple like you and like I. I won-der as I wan-der out un-der the sky.

2. When Mary birth'd Jesus, 'twas in a cow's stall
   with wise men and farmers and shepherds and all.
   But high from God's heaven a star's light did fall,
   and the promise of ages it did then recall.

3. If Jesus had wanted for any wee thing,
   a star in the sky, or a bird on the wing,
   or all of God's angels in heav'n for to sing,
   he surely could have it, 'cause he was the king.

Text and Melody: Traditional North American

CHRIST WAS BORN ON CHRISTMAS DAY

1. Christ was born on Christ-mas Day; wreathe the hol-ly, twine the bay, Chris-tus na-tus

ho-di-e, the babe, the son, the ho-ly one of Ma-ry.

2. He is born to set us free;
   he is born our Lord to be,
   ex Maria virgine,
   the God, the Lord,
   by all adored for ever.

3. Let the bright red berries glow
   everywhere in goodly show,
   Christus natus hodie,
   the babe, the son,
   the holy one of Mary.

4. Christians all, rejoice and sing;
   'tis the birthday of the King,
   ex Maria virgine,
   the God, the Lord,
   by all adored for ever.

Text: John Mason Neale (1818 - 1866)
Melody: From *Piae Cantiones* (1582)

DING DONG! MERRILY ON HIGH

2. E'en so, here below, below, let steeple bells be swungen,
   and io, io, io, by priest and people sungen.

3. Pray you, dutifully prime your matin chime, ye ringers;
   may you beautifully rime your eve-time song, ye singers.

Text: George Ratcliffe Woodward (1848 - 1934)
Melody: Traditional French

IN DULCI JUBILO

1. In dul - ci ju - bi - lo, let us our ho - mage show; our heart's joy re -
cli - neth in prae - se - pi - o and like a bright star shi - neth ma -
tris in gre - mi - o. Al - pha es et O, Al - pha es et O.

2. O Jesu parvule!
   I yearn for thee alway!
   Hear me, I beseech thee,
   O puer optime!
   My prayer let it reach thee,
   O Princeps gloriae!
   Trahe me post te,
   trahe me post te!

3. O Patris caritas.
   O Nati lenitas!
   Deeply were we stained
   per nostra crimina;
   but thou hast for us gained
   caelorum gaudia.
   O that we were there,
   O that we were there!

4. Ubi sunt gaudia,
   if that they be not there?
   There are angels singing
   nova cantica,
   there the bells are ringing
   in regis curia:
   O that we were there,
   O that we were there!

Text: Translated from the German by Robert Lucas Pearsall (1795 - 1856)
Melody: From Klug's *Geistliche Lieder* (1535)

SEE AMID THE WINTER'S SNOW

2. Lo, within a manger lies
   he who built the starry skies;
   he who, throned in heights sublime,
   sits amid the cherubim.

3. Say, ye holy shepherds, say,
   what your joyful news today?
   Wherefore have ye left your sheep
   on the lonely mountain steep?

4. 'As we watched at dead of night,
   lo, we saw a wondrous light;
   angels, singing peace on earth,
   told us of the Saviour's birth.'

5. Sacred infant, all divine,
   what a tender love was thine,
   thus to come from highest bliss,
   down to such a world as this!

6. Teach, O teach us, holy child,
   by thy face so meek and mild,
   teach us to resemble thee,
   in thy sweet humility.

Text: Edward Caswall (1814 - 1878)
Melody: John Goss (1800 - 1880)

GOD REST YOU MERRY, GENTLEMEN

1. God rest you merry, gentlemen, let nothing you dismay, for

Jesus Christ our Saviour was born on Christmas Day, to save us all from

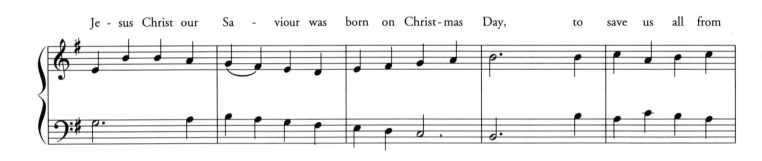

Satan's pow'r when we were gone astray: *Refrain* O tidings of comfort and

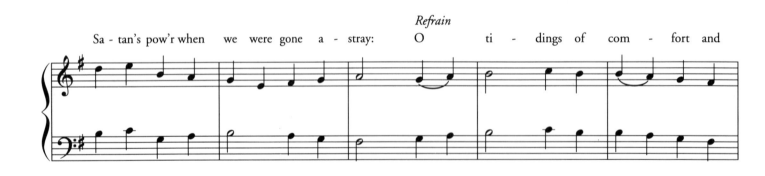

joy, comfort and joy, O tidings of comfort and joy.

2. In Bethlehem in Jewry
   the blessed babe was born,
   and laid within a manger,
   upon this blessed morn;
   the which his mother Mary
   did nothing take in scorn.

3. From God our heav'nly Father
   a blessed angel came,
   and unto certain shepherds
   brought tidings of the same,
   now that in Bethlehem was born
   the Son of God by name.

4. 'Fear not,' then said the angel,
   'Let nothing you affright,
   this day is born a Saviour
   of virtue, pow'r and might;
   so frequently to vanquish all
   the friends of Satan quite.'

5. The shepherds at those tidings
   rejoiced much in mind,
   and left their flocks a-feeding,
   in tempest, storm and wind,
   and went to Bethlehem straight-way
   this blessed babe to find.

6. But when to Bethlehem they came,
   whereat this infant lay,
   they found him in a manger,
   where oxen feed on hay;
   his mother Mary kneeling,
   unto the Lord did pray.

7. Now to the Lord sing praises,
   all you within this place,
   and with true love and brotherhood
   each other now embrace;
   this holy tide of Christmas
   all others doth deface.

Text: Unknown
Melody: Traditional English

THE SANS DAY CAROL

2. Now the holly bears a berry
   as green as the grass,
   and Mary bore Jesus,
   who died on the cross.

3. Now the holly bears a berry
   as black as the coal,
   and Mary bore Jesus,
   who died for us all.

4. Now the holly bears a berry
   as blood it is red,
   then trust we our Saviour,
   who rose from the dead.

Text: Collected by Percy Dearmer (1867 - 1936)
Melody: Traditional Cornish

WHILE SHEPHERDS WATCHED THEIR FLOCKS

2. 'Fear not,' said he, (for mighty dread
   had seized their troubled mind)
   'glad tidings of great joy I bring
   to you and all mankind.

3. To you, in David's town this day
   is born of David's line
   a Saviour who is Christ the Lord;
   and this shall be the sign:

4. The heavenly babe you there shall find
   to human view displayed,
   all meanly wrapped in swathing bands,
   and in a manger laid.'

5. Thus spake the seraph, and forthwith
   appeared a shining throng
   of angels praising God, who thus
   addressed their joyful song:

6. 'All glory be to God on high,
   and on the earth be peace;
   goodwill henceforth from heaven
   to men begin and never cease.'

Text: Nahum Tate (1652 - 1715)
Melody: From Thomas Este's *Psalmes* (1592)

WE WISH YOU A MERRY CHRISTMAS

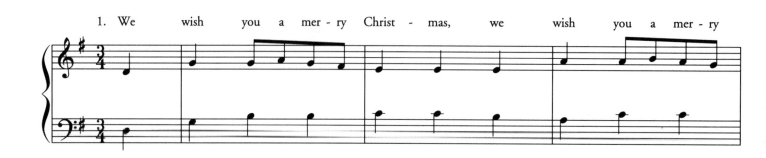

1. We wish you a mer-ry Christ-mas, we wish you a mer-ry

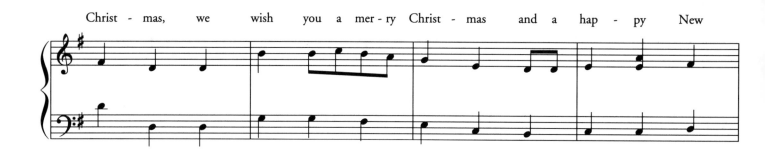

Christ-mas, we wish you a mer-ry Christ-mas and a hap-py New

Year! *Refrain* Good tid-ings we bring to you and your

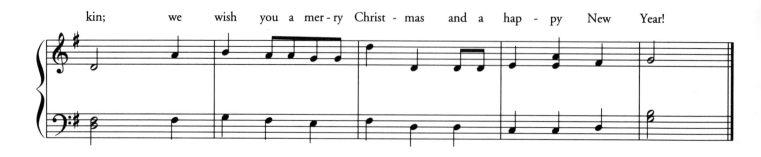

kin; we wish you a mer-ry Christ-mas and a hap-py New Year!

2. Now bring us some figgy pudding,
   now bring us some figgy pudding,
   now bring us some figgy pudding,
   and bring some out here.

3. We all like figgy pudding,
   we all like figgy pudding,
   we all like figgy pudding,
   so bring some out here.

4. We won't go till we've got some,
   we won't go till we've got some,
   we won't go till we've got some,
   so bring some out here.

Text and Melody: Traditional English

SILENT NIGHT

1. Si - lent night, ho - ly night. All is calm, all is bright,

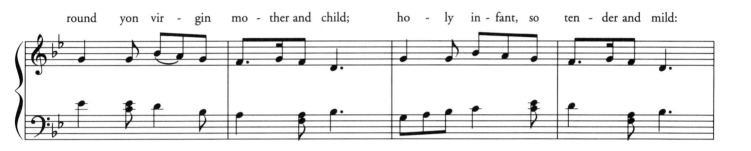

round yon vir - gin mo - ther and child; ho - ly in - fant, so ten - der and mild:

sleep in hea - ven - ly peace, sleep in hea - ven - ly peace.

2. Silent night, holy night.
   Shepherds quake at the sight,
   glories stream from heaven afar,
   heavenly hosts sing alleluia:
   Christ, the Saviour is born,
   Christ, the Saviour is born.

3. Silent night, holy night.
   Son of God, love's pure light
   radiant beams from thy holy face,
   with the dawn of redeeming grace:
   Jesus, Lord, at thy birth,
   Jesus, Lord at thy birth.

Text: Joseph Möhr (1792 - 1848) translated by John Freeman Young (1820 - 1885)
Melody: Franz Grüber (1787 - 1863)

THE FIRST NOWELL

2. They looked up and saw a star,
   shining in the east, beyond them far;
   and to the earth it gave great light,
   and so it continued both day and night.

3. And by the light of that same star,
   three wise men came from country far;
   to seek for a king was their intent,
   and to follow the star wherever it went.

4. This star drew nigh to the north-west;
   o'er Bethlehem it took its rest,
   and there it did both stop and stay
   right over the place where Jesus lay.

5. Then entered in those wise men three,
   full reverently upon their knee,
   and offered there in his presence
   their gold and myrrh and frankincense.

6. Then let us all with one accord
   sing praises to our heavenly Lord,
   that hath made heaven and earth of naught,
   and with his blood mankind hath bought.

Text and Melody: Traditional English

COVENTRY CAROL

2. Herod, the king, in his raging,
   chargèd he hath this day
   his men of might, in his own sight,
   all young children to slay.

3. That woe is me, poor child for thee!
   And ever morn and day,
   for thy parting neither say nor sing,
   by by, lully lullay!

Text: Robert Croo (c.1534)
Melody: From the *Pageant of the Shearmen and Tailors* (15th Century)

GOOD CHRISTIANS ALL, REJOICE

2. Good Christians all, rejoice
with heart and soul and voice!
Hear the news of endless bliss,
Jesus Christ was born for this:
he has opened heaven's door,
and we are blessed for evermore!
Christ was born for this,
Christ was born for this.

3. Good Christians all, rejoice
with heart and soul and voice!
Now you need not fear the grave,
Jesus Christ was born to save:
come at his most gracious call
to find salvation, one and all:
Christ was born to save,
Christ was born to save!

Text: John Mason Neale (1818 - 1866)
Melody: From Klug's *Geistliche Lieder* (1535)

INFANT HOLY, INFANT LOWLY

1. In-fant ho - ly, in-fant low - ly, for his bed a cat-tle stall; ox-en low - ing, lit-tle know - ing Christ the babe is Lord of all. Swift are wing - ing an - gels sing - ing, no-wells ring - ing, tid-ings bring - ing, Christ the babe is Lord of all, Christ the babe is Lord of all.

2. Flocks were sleeping, shepherds keeping
vigil till the morning new;
saw the glory, heard the story
tidings of a gospel true.
Thus rejoicing, free from sorrow,
praises voicing, greet the morrow,
Christ the babe was born for you,
Christ the babe was born for you!

Text: Translated from the Polish by Edith Margaret Reed (1885 - 1933)
Melody: Traditional Polish

ANGELS FROM THE REALMS OF GLORY

2. Shepherds in the fields abiding,
   watching o'er your flocks by night,
   God with man is now residing;
   yonder shines the infant Light.

3. Sages, leave your contemplation;
   brighter visions beam afar;
   seek the great Desire of Nations:
   ye have seen his natal star.

4. Saints before the altar bending,
   watching long in hope and fear,
   suddenly the Lord, descending,
   in his temple shall appear.

5. Though an infant now we view him,
   he shall fill his Father's throne,
   gather all the nations to him;
   every knee shall then bow down.

Text: James Montgomery (1771 - 1854)
Melody: Traditional French

AWAY IN A MANGER

2. The cattle are lowing, the baby awakes,
   but little Lord Jesus no crying he makes
   I love thee, Lord Jesus! Look down from the sky,
   and stay by my side until morning is nigh.

3. Be near me, Lord Jesus, I ask you to stay
   close by me for ever, and love me, I pray.
   Bless all the dear children in your tender care,
   and fit us for heaven, to live with thee there.

Text: Luther's Cradle Hymn (c.1885)
Melody: William James Kirkpatrick (1838 - 1921)

O COME ALL YE FAITHFUL

1. O come, all ye faith - ful, joy - ful and tri - um - phant, O come ye, O come ye to Beth - le - hem; come and be - hold him born the king of an - gels:

Refrain

O come, let us a - dore him, O come, let us a - dore him, O come let us a - dore him, Christ the Lord.

2. God of God,
   Light of Light,
   lo! he abhors not the virgin's womb;
   very God, begotten, not created.

3. Sing, choirs of angels,
   sing in exultation,
   sing all ye citizens of heav'n above:
   'Glory to God in the highest.'

4. Yea, Lord, we greet thee,
   born this happy morning,
   Jesu, to thee be glory given;
   word of the Father, now in flesh appearing.

Text: Translated from the Latin by Frederick Oakeley (1802 - 1880)
Melody: Probably by John Francis Wade (1711 - 1786)